LITTLE SISTER

PLAYGROUND GAMES

THIS BOOK BELONGS TO

_____

Look for these and other books about Karen in the Baby-sitters Little Sister series:

BABY-SITTERS

LITTLE SISTER

PLAYGROUND GAMES

ANN M. MARTIN

A
LITTLE APPLE
PAPERBACK

SCHOLASTIC INC.
NEW YORK TORONTO LONDON AUCKLAND SYDNEY

*The author gratefully acknowledges
Nancy E. Krulik for her help
with this book.*

Cover art by Susan Tang
Interior art by John Devore

ISBN 0-590-74131-4

12 11 10 9 8 7 6 5 4 3 2   6 7 8 9/9 01/0

Printed in the U.S.A.   40

First Scholastic printing, July 1996

CONTENTS

READY OR NOT,
HERE COMES KAREN!

What do you like to do on the playground? Play hopscotch? Tell jokes? Play jacks?

Karen, Hannie, Nancy, and the other kids in Ms. Colman's class know a lot of terrific playground games. This book is filled with their favorites. Some of the games are games you can play all by yourself. Some are games for lots of players. You and your friends can use the special Baby-sitters Little Sister chalk, ball, jacks, and string in this package to play many of the games.

So what are you waiting for? Turn the page, and *let the games begin*!

HAVIN' A BALL!

Karen didn't know how much fun ball games could be until she joined Kristy's Krushers, the softball team coached by her big sister, Kristy. Karen even hit a home run! Now Home Run Karen loves any game that uses a ball. You will, too!

Okay, everybody ... PLAY BALL!

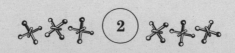

SNAPPER CLAPPER
a game for one player

Whether it's for her great spelling in the finals of the Stoneybrook spelling bee, or her silly dancing in the Thanksgiving play, Karen loves applause. Maybe that's why she loves this hand-clapping ball game. You'll learn the rules in a snap!

You will need:
  one ball

Here's how you play:

1. Toss the ball in the air.
2 Clap your hands one time.
3. Catch the ball.
4. Toss the ball again.
5. Clap your hands two times.
6. Catch the ball again.
7. Keep on playing, adding one clap each time you toss the ball.

How many times can you clap before you miss?

Karen's helpful hint:
  Practice with a larger ball before you try this with the small ball in the *Baby-sitters Little Sister Playground Games* Kit.

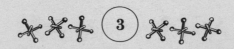

STONEYBROOK SQUARES

(also known as Four-Square)
a game for four players

You need to play this super squares game on cement or asphalt — a playground would be just the right place!

You will need:

chalk, a large rubber kick ball

The setup:

Use your chalk to draw four squares as you see in the picture below. Each side of each square should be three feet long. Label your squares A, B, C, D just as in the picture.

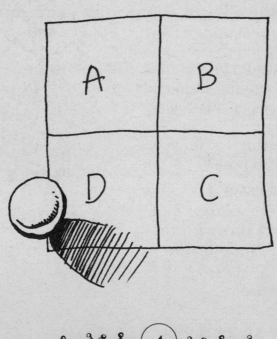

Here's how you play:

1. Each player stands in a square. The person at square A is the server. The goal of every player is to become the server. You do that by making the other players miss. That way, you can move around the squares, from D to C to B and then to square A.
2. The server bounces the ball and hits it into someone else's square.
3. That person waits for the ball to bounce, and then hits it into another square. The players continue to hit the ball until a player misses. A player misses if she doesn't hit the ball into another square on the first bounce. A player also misses if she hits the ball and it lands outside one of the squares. (If the ball lands on the line it is not a miss.)
4. The player who misses must *always* move to square D. Everyone else moves up to the next available square.
5. The server serves the ball again.
6. Keep playing until the bell rings and recess is over. Everyone wins at Stoneybrook Squares!

Karen's helpful hint:

Here's an easy way to pick who will serve first: Since Baby-sitters Little Sister #1, *Karen's Witch*, was published in August 1988, choose the person whose birthday is closest to August 1.

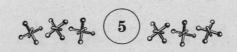

Variation of this game

Think of a category and then scream out something that fits into that category as you hit the ball to another player. If you can't think of something that fits into the category, or if you repeat an item someone else has already said, you've missed.

Here's an example: The category is boys' names. Some are: Ricky, Andrew, David Michael, and Bobby.

Here's another example: The category is cereals. Some are: Froot Loops, Cap'n Crunch, Frosted Flakes, and Rice Krispies.

SPUD!

a game for four or more players

'or a while, Karen was afraid to play Spud with ьobby Gianelli, because Bobby was a bully. He threw the ball too hard. But once Bobby realized the game was just for fun, he stopped trying to hurt the other players. (You should keep that in mind when you play, too.) Now this is one of Karen's and Bobby's favorite games.

You will need:

a soft rubber ball

Here's how you play:

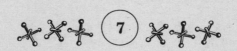

1. Choose one person to be "It." Everyone else forms a circle around the person who is "It."

2. The person who is "It" throws the ball up in the air. Everyone else scatters. When the person who is "It" catches the ball he or she yells, "Spud!" Everyone else must freeze where they are.

3. Now the person who is "It" can take three giant steps toward the closest player and try to hit that player with the ball.

4. If the person who is "It" hits the other player, that player gets an "S," and is now "It." If the person who is "It" misses, he or she has to go again until "It" hits someone with the ball.

5. Continue to play this way. Every time a player gets hit with the ball, he or she gets a letter until someone gets S-P-U-D, and the game is over.

FLIP THE PENNY
a game for two players

When Karen found a penny (faceup, of course) it brought her luck — both good and bad. On the one hand, she got lucky and found a wallet filled with money. She even earned reward money by turning the wallet in. But Karen had some bad luck, too. She spent all the reward money and almost didn't get to go to her favorite amusement park.

If you find a penny, faceup or facedown, pick it up and use it to play this lucky penny game.

You will need:

a soft rubber ball, a penny, two sidewalk squares with a crack in the middle

Here's how you play:

1. Place the penny faceup on the crack between the sidewalk squares.
2. The players stand behind the lines of the two sidewalk squares, as you see in the picture.
3. The first player bounces the ball, trying to hit the penny on the bounce. If the penny flips over, that player gets one point.
4. Place the penny back on the crack. Now it is the other player's turn.
5. Keep playing until one player has 10 points.

Karen's helpful hint:

Don't bounce the ball too hard. A gentle bounce that hits the edge of the penny will flip it right over.

STEAL THE BACON

a game for eight or more players

Karen knows stealing is bad — after all, she was pretty sad when her bike was stolen. But when you play this game, stealing's not only allowed, it's the only way to win!

You will need:
   a soft rubber ball

Here's how you play:
1. Split the players into two equal teams. (Karen sometimes calls the teams the Three Musketeers and the Milky Ways, but you can give your teams any names you want.)
2. Choose one player to be the caller.
3. Each player on a team is given a number.
4. The teams stand in two straight lines, facing each other on opposite sides of the playing field.
5. The caller places the ball in the middle of the field. Then he or she calls out a number. The players from both teams who have been given that number run up to the ball.

6. The players try to grab the ball ("the bacon"). The player who grabs the ball first runs back to her team line. If she gets back without being tagged by the other player, her team gets the point. But if she is tagged by the other player, his team gets the point.
7. Keep playing until one team has 20 points.

Karen's helpful hint:

If you think you are a faster runner than your opponent, try to steal the bacon. But it's not always good to be the one who "steals the bacon." Picking up the ball slows you down. So if you think you are the slower runner, wait and try to be the one to tag your opponent.

BOUNCING RHYMES

a game for one player

These rhymes are great. They really rate. So get your ball. Do not wait!

You will need:
a soft rubber ball

Here's how you play:
Bounce the ball with the palm of your hand. As the ball bounces in the air, turn your leg over the ball. Do not hit the ball with your leg. Say these rhymes as you bounce the ball.

CANDY IS DANDY

Hippity hop to the sweet shop

to buy a bar of candy.

One for Karen, one for Nancy,

and one, of course, for Hannie.

(You can use the names of your pals instead of Karen, Nancy, and Hannie.)

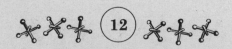

DOCTOR, DOCTOR

One, two, three a nation.
Doctor, doctor there's a patient,
waiting for an operation.
One, two, three a nation.

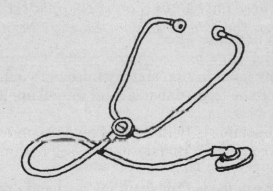

DO YOU LOVE ME?

Do you love me
or do you not?
You told me once
but I forgot.

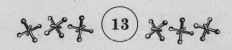

THE ALPHABET RHYME
a game for one player

Here is one more bouncing rhyme. As you bounce the ball, try to come up with names, places, and objects for each letter of the alphabet. You have to turn your leg over the ball only on each alphabet word. Karen's given you a head start — here are her ideas for A, B, and C.

A my name is Ann and my husband's name is Andrew. We come from Alabama, and we sell apples.

B my name is Bethany and my husband's name is Bill. We come from Buffalo, and we sell bathing suits.

C my name is Cindy and my husband's name is Carlos. We come from California, and we sell cabbages.

IT'S JOKE TIME

Karen loves jokes — on April Fool's Day or any day. So take a break from all these ball games and have a good laugh!

Why did "icky" Ricky put on a wet shirt?
Because the label said wash and wear!

Why should baby Daniel be allowed to cry?
If he isn't, he could get back-tear-ia!

Why did Hannie put her father in the refrigerator?
Because she wanted a cold pop!

Why did Kristy start taking tennis lessons?
She likes raising a racket!

HOT POTATO

a game for three or more players

Karen had a great summer at Camp Mohawk. She and her friends sang songs, played games, and had yummy cookouts. One time they baked potatoes over a fire. The potatoes were so hot that even the counselors were afraid to touch them. Watching the counselors throw the hot potatoes in the air reminded Karen of this really cool game!

You will need:

a ball, a radio or a tape player

Here's how you play:

1. All the players stand in a circle. One person stands outside the circle. He or she will be the disk jockey.
2. The disk jockey turns on the radio.
3. As soon as the music starts, the players begin throwing the ball to one another.
4. When the music stops, the person holding the ball (the hot potato) is out.
5. Keep playing until there is only one player left. That player is the hottest potato of all — the winner!

ALL BALL TALL TALES

a game for three or more players

Karen, Hannie, and Nancy love to write stories. They even had their own newspaper for a while — The 3M Gazette (named for the Three Musketeers, of course)! But the girls got into big trouble when they published secrets about their neighbors. So now the girls stick to making up silly stories. You and your friends can make them up, too!

You will need:

a ball

Here's how you play:

Sit in a circle. The first player holds the ball and begins the story. The story can be about anything, and each player can talk for as long as she wants. She just can't finish the story. Instead, when she reaches a really exciting part, she should pass the ball to the next player. The next player can continue the story in whatever way he chooses, until he passes the ball to the player next to him. The last player to have a turn finishes the story.

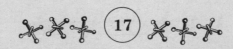

ARE YOU THIRSTY?

Here are some yummy drink ideas for you and your friends. They come straight from Karen's gigundoly successful lemonade stand.

PINEAPPLE PUNCH WITH A PUNCH!

You will need:

4 cups cranberry juice, 3 cups apple juice, 1/2 cup lemon juice, 1 cup pineapple tidbits, 1 bottle seltzer, a mixing spoon, a mixing bowl, ice

Here's what you do:

Mix all the juices together in the mixing bowl. Pour in the pineapple tidbits. Just before serving time, pour in the seltzer. Stir and serve over ice.

(Serves 8)

LEMON SIPPER

You will need:

1 large lemon, 1 hollow peppermint candy stick

Here's what you do:

Roll the lemon between your hands. This will soften the pulp. Ask a grown-up to cut the top off of your lemon. Stick the peppermint candy stick into the lemon. Use the candy stick as a straw to suck out the lemon juice.

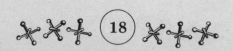

VERY CHERRY BERRY PUNCH

You will need:

1 envelope cherry-flavored drink mix, 3 cups cold water, 1 8-ounce can pineapple juice, 3 tablespoons lemon juice, 1 pint raspberry sherbet, a mixing spoon, a mixing bowl

Here's what you do:

Mix the drink mix in the water and stir until the drink mix is dissolved. Pour in the pineapple and lemon juice. Fill 10-ounce glasses halfway with your mixture. Top off each drink with two scoops of sherbet.

(Serves 10)

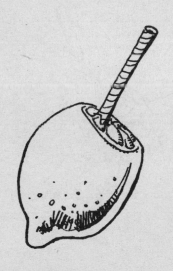

CHALK TALK!

Oh, no! Karen is writing on the sidewalk. And Andrew the tattletale is going to tell on her. Don't worry. Karen won't be in trouble — she's using sidewalk chalk. She can wash it away when she is through.

Karen uses her sidewalk chalk to draw all kinds of playing fields on the playground. Here are some of her favorite sidewalk chalk games.

Okay, everybody...write on!

FOX AND FEATHERS

**(also known as Fox and Geese or Fox and Ducklings)
a game for five or more players**

Ms. Colman's class watched a duck named Feather hatch her eggs. When the ducklings were old enough to go out on their own, the class set them free. Karen loved Feather so much that she changed the name of her favorite game, Fox and Ducklings, to Fox and Feathers.

You will need:

sidewalk chalk

The setup:

Draw a circle about 20 feet around. This is your wheel. Then add six spokes to your wheel as you see in the picture. The spot where the spokes meet is called the safety spot.

Here's how you play:

1. Choose one player to be the fox. Everyone else is a duck.
2. The fox chases the ducks around the wheel, trying to tag one of them. The ducks are allowed to jump across from one spoke to another. The fox's feet cannot leave the drawn lines. He must chase the ducks around the wheel or up and down the spokes.
3. Only one duck at a time can stand on the safety spot. A duck in the safety spot cannot be tagged. If another duck steps on the safety spot, the duck that was there is no longer safe from the fox.
4. Any duck tagged by the fox becomes the fox, and the game begins again.

DRAW IT!

a game for four or more players

Nannie likes to say, "A picture is worth a thousand words." Karen isn't sure what that means, but she does like to play this game, in which a picture helps you guess the words.

You will need:
sidewalk chalk, paper, pencil, a small paper lunch bag, a one-minute egg timer

The setup:
Before your friends show up, write down the things you would like them to draw during the game. You can use the names of your favorite TV shows, books, songs, or movies. You can use familiar sayings, too. Write down eight different drawing ideas on separate slips of paper. Then fold up the slips and place them in the bag. Once everyone is ready to play, divide into two equal teams.

Here's how you play:
1. The first team decides who will be the artist. That person will draw the pictures, and everyone else on the team will try to guess what she is drawing.
2. The artist picks one slip of paper from the bag.
3. Turn over the egg timer.

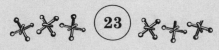

4. Using the chalk, the artist must draw a picture that helps her teammates guess what she is drawing. She cannot talk, she cannot use hand signals, and she cannot use letters to spell out the words.

5. As the artist draws, her teammates look at the drawings to try to guess what's written on the slip of paper. They have one minute to guess. They can guess as many things as they want. If they figure out the drawing before one minute is up, the team gets one point. If they cannot guess, the other team has one chance to try and figure out what is written on the paper and earn the point.

6. After all eight pictures are drawn, the team with the most points wins.

Karen's helpful hints:

When it is Karen's turn to come up with the ideas for the drawings, she likes to use the titles of her favorite books. Here are three of them: *Charlotte's Web*, *The Cut-ups*, and *Pippi Longstocking*.

Hannie likes to write down people and things she sees in Stoneybrook, such as the letter carrier, the sidewalk, or a jump rope.

Nancy loves going to the movies. When it is her turn to pick the words, she uses movie titles such as *A Little Princess*, *Pinocchio*, and *Home Alone*.

DOTS ALL!

games for two players

Karen first learned to play dot games when she, Hannie, and Nancy went on vacation to Shadow Lake. Back then, she played the games on paper. But dot games are even more fun when you play them on a really big space, such as a sidewalk square. Here are two fun dot games to try.

SQUARE DOTS

You will need:
  sidewalk chalk

The setup:
  Draw rows of dots like you see in the picture below. (Don't draw the lines. Karen and Hannie put them there to show you how to play the game.)

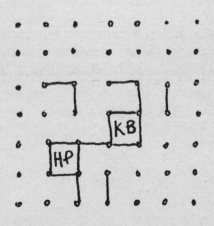

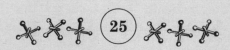

Here's how you play:

1. The first player draws a line anywhere — either up, down, or sideways from one dot to the one next to it.
2. The next player does the same thing. The object of the game is to draw a line that will complete a box. If you draw the last line on any box, a box is yours. Put your initial inside the box. Then you get to go again. Draw a new line.
3. When all the boxes have been completed, the game is over. The player with the most boxes is the winner.

Karen's helpful hint:

Sometimes it's fun to draw hearts or stars instead of dots. Then the players connect the hearts or the stars to make the squares.

TRIANGLE DOTS

You will need:
sidewalk chalk

The setup:
Draw rows of dots in a triangle shape as you see on the opposite page. (Don't draw the lines. Karen and Hannie put them there to show you how to play the game.)

Here's how you play:

1. The first player draws a line, either up, down, sideways, or diagonally to the dot next to it.
2. The next player does the same thing. The object of the game is to draw a line that will complete a triangle. If you draw the last line on any triangle, it is yours. Put your initial inside the triangle. Then you get to go again. Draw a new line.
3. Once all the dots are connected, the player with the most triangles is the winner.

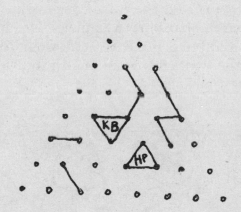

SNACK ATTACK!

You must be hungry after playing all these games. Why not stop for a while for a fun-to-do fondue? Kristy and Karen make this together during the months Karen stays at the big house.

You will need:

1 cup plain yogurt, 2 tablespoons orange juice concentrate, small bowl brown sugar, toothpicks, fruit such as fresh strawberries, pineapple chunks, apple chunks, pear chunks, banana slices, or grapes, mixing bowl

Here's what you do:

Mix the yogurt and the juice concentrate together in a bowl. Serve the fruit on toothpicks. Dip the fruit into the yogurt-and-juice mixture and then roll it in the sugar. Pop the fruit into your mouth (but be very careful of the toothpicks).

LEFT, RIGHT, LEFT, RIGHT
a parade for two or more players

Ever since she learned to play the tuba, Karen has wanted to march in a band. Even if you don't know how to play an instrument, you can have your own march-in-place parade. All you need is some chalk, two feet, and a loud voice!

You will need:

sidewalk chalk

The setup:

Place your feet firmly on the ground. Ask a friend to trace around your feet with the chalk. Do the same thing for your pal. Keep tracing each other's feet until you each have left a long trail of footprints. Now you're ready to march!

Here's what you do:

Put your right foot in the drawing of your right foot. Put your left foot in the drawing of your left foot. Start marching along your trail to the rhythm of your favorite rhyme.

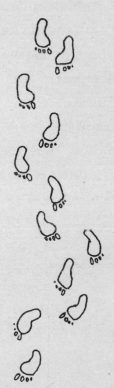

Karen's helpful hint:

Here is one of Karen's favorite marching rhymes. Can you think of any of your own?

THE DOUGHNUT RHYME

I had a nickel and I walked around the block.

I walked right into the bakery shop.

I grabbed a doughnut right from the grease,

and handed the lady the five-cent piece.

The lady looked at the nickel and she looked at me.

She said, "This money's no good to me.

There's a hole in the nickel and it goes straight through."

Said I, "There's a hole in the doughnut, too!"

Thanks for the doughnut.

So long.

HOPSCOTCH

a game for two or more players

Karen loves hopscotch. In fact, she has a special stone that she uses just to play the game. Take a look at Karen's helpful hint below and you'll find out how to make your own special hopscotch stone.

You will need:

sidewalk chalk, a hopscotch stone

The setup:

Draw a hopscotch diagram like the one you see below. It should be about 10 feet long. Every box should be the same size.

Here's how you play:

1. The first player tosses her hopscotch stone into box 1.

2. Using one foot, the player hops over box 1 and into boxes 2 and 3, landing on both feet (one in box 2 and one in box 3) at the same time.

3. Then she hops to box 4, then to boxes 5 and 6 (placing one foot in box 5 and one foot in box 6.) The player keeps going, landing with only one foot in each box, until she lands in box 10.

4. The player hops up, spins in the air, and lands in the opposite direction with the same foot in box 10. She then hops back through all the boxes until she reaches boxes 2 and 3.

5. The player bends over on two feet, picks up her hopscotch stone, and jumps off. If she gets all the way to the end without stepping on a line, placing two feet in one box, falling, or missing a box, she may throw her stone at box number 2 and repeat what she has done, this time skipping box 2.

6. If a player misses during a turn, or if her stone lands in the wrong box, she should place her stone into the last box she played. Her turn is over, and the next player has a turn. The first player to finish is the winner.

Karen's helpful hint:

Karen's lucky hopscotch stone has helped her become a champion hopper. You can make a gigundoly cool hopscotch stone, too. Start with a stone that is not too round. Round stones often roll when they land. Take a piece of sandpaper and smooth your stone on all sides until it shines. Then, take a permanent marker and print the first letter of your name on the stone — that way everyone will know it's yours! If you want, use other permanent markers to decorate your special hopscotch stone.

IT'S JOKE TIME AGAIN!

Here are three favorite jokes from the Three Musketeers. Which makes you laugh the hardest?

Karen's joke:

What kind of elephant can you find in a box of popcorn?
A very small one!

Hannie's joke:

Who had a time-out for causing trouble?
Hankie Pankie!

Nancy's joke:

Nancy: How many famous people were born in New York City?
Karen: I don't know. How many?
Nancy: None—only babies!

FREEZE TAG

a game for five or more players

When Karen went to Shadow Lake with her big-house family, she found out she didn't like skiing at all! But Karen likes a lot of other winter games, such as ice skating and making ice sculptures. Sometimes Karen is sad when the weather turns warm and winter disappears. But at least she can play this cool game all year long!

You will need:
    sidewalk chalk

The setup:
    Use your chalk to draw a starting line.

Here's how you play:

1. Choose one person to be "It." "It" stands about 50 feet from the starting line. Everyone else stands behind the starting line.

2. "It" turns his back on the other players and counts to 10. As he counts, everyone starts to run closer to him.

3. When "It" reaches 10, he turns around quickly. All the others have to freeze in the exact position they were in when "It" reached the number 10.

4. Anyone who moves (even a teensy-weensy bit) goes back to the starting line.

5. "It" turns around and begins counting again.

6. As soon as any player is close enough to tag "It," she should. Then all the players have to run back toward the starting line.

7. If a player is tagged by "It" before she reaches the starting line, she becomes the new "It" and the game begins again.

SUPER SILLY PUZZLE
24 - 8 = 2

This is not the arithmetic you learn in Ms. Colman's class. In fact, it's not arithmetic at all. It is a trick Karen thought up to fool her best enemy, Pamela. Try it yourself. Then look on page 69 for Karen's answer.

You will need:
sidewalk chalk, a chalk eraser or a damp sponge

The setup:
Draw nine squares as you see in the picture.

The puzzle:
Can you remove eight lines and leave only two squares?

SPEAK UP!

Karen often forgets to use her indoor voice. (She *never* forgets to use her outdoor voice.) You will have to use both of your voices when you play these games!

What was that you said? I can't hear you. Speak up!

WHISPERING DOWN THE LANE

a game for six or more players

Karen is always getting in trouble for spying on people—especially her next-door neighbor, Morbidda Destiny. The problem is that Karen never sees what she thinks she's seen. And she never hears what she thinks she's heard. What do you think you've heard?

Here's how you play:
1. Everyone stands side by side in a line.
2. The first player in line makes up a sentence.
3. The person who makes up the sentence whispers it to the next person in line, who whispers it to the next person, and so on.

4. If a player cannot hear or understand what is whispered in her ear, she must say, "Operator!" The person before her must whisper the sentence again.
5. The last person in line must shout out the sentence he has heard. It probably won't sound at all like the sentence that was first whispered down the lane.
6. Now have everyone line up in a new order, and play the game again.

Karen's helpful hint:

Try to begin this game with a sentence in three parts. The sentence should begin with someone's name, where that person is, and what he or she is doing. You could say something like: Nancy was in her house changing baby Danny's diapers. (Yuck!)

KNOT BAD!

(also known as The Human Knot)
a game for six or more players

At Camp Mohawk, Karen learned to pitch a tent and sleep out in the woods. She also learned to make all sorts of knots. Karen can tie and untie square knots, bowline knots, and even half hitch knots. In fact, the only knot she has trouble untying is this knot of kids!

The setup:

Everyone stands in a circle. Each player uses his right hand to hold the hand of someone who is not standing next to him. Then each player uses his left hand to hold someone else's hand. Now everybody is all tangled up.

Here's how you play:

Everyone shares a tough job — to untangle the human knot and make a perfect circle again, where everyone is holding hands with the person standing next to her. That's not as easy as it sounds, because you can't let go of one another's hands. You have to make a circle by climbing over and under one another's arms and legs. And since you can't use your hands to give directions, you'll have to use words.

JOHN JACOB JINGLEHEIMER SCHMIDT

a silly song for one or more singers

Karen sings this song wherever she goes — at the little house or the big house. After all, Karen is a two-two. And this song lets her use two voices — indoor and outdoor!

Here's how you sing the song:

Sing the whole song loudly at first. Then sing it over and over again. Each time you do, sing a little more softly. Just be sure to shout out, "La la la la la la la!" every time you sing the song.

John Jacob Jingleheimer Schmidt

That's my name, too.

Whenever we go out

The people always shout

There goes John Jacob Jingleheimer Schmidt.

La la la la la la la !

ANOTHER SNACK ATTACK!

Do you remember when Karen was named Pizza Queen at Pizza Express? She got to wear a crown, be in a commercial, and have her picture on a big billboard. Of course, Karen bragged so much about all the fun she was having that the Pizza Queen became a royal pain! Try this tasty pizza snack. It's fit for a king or a queen.

You will need:

half a hero roll, one small can of tomato sauce, mozzarella cheese, mushrooms, pepperoni, meatballs, broccoli, green pepper, garlic powder

Here's what you do:

1. Ask a grown-up to preheat your oven to 350°.
2. Scoop out the inside of the bread until it looks like a bread boat.
3. Now pour the sauce, cheese, and toppings into your bread boat.
4. Place your pizza on a cookie sheet.
5. Ask a grown-up to place your pizza in the oven and bake it until the cheese melts and the sauce is hot (about five to eight minutes).
6. Have the grown-up remove your pizza from the oven. Let it cool just a bit and then dig in! Yummy!

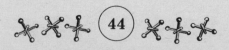

THE POISONOUS
PEANUT BUTTER PIT
a game for two players

Morbidda Destiny likes to work in her garden. But Karen would never eat anything from that garden. Who knows, the vegetables could be covered with witch's poison. In fact, the whole garden could be a ... Poisonous Peanut Butter Pit!

You will need:

a blindfold, a baseball bat, a large ball, a big pillow, a chair, a jump rope, the string from this package, and anything else you would like to use for an obstacle course

The setup:

Use all of the items except the blindfold to create an obstacle course. Spread them out all over the playground.

Here's how you play:

Pretend the items on the ground are made of poisonous peanut butter. You don't want to touch any of them. Blindfold one player. The other player must lead the blindfolded player through the obstacle course. But here's the catch. The players cannot touch. The player who can see must direct her pal over, under, and around the obstacles by talking to her.

NUTTY NAMES

a game for six or more players

It's not easy being the new kid in school. When Addie Sidney first came to Ms. Colman's class, she had to learn a lot of names. So Ms. Colman taught the class how to play this name game. After playing the game, Addie knew everyone!

The setup:

Have all of the players sit in a circle.

Here's how you play:

1. The first player says her own name out loud. She follows it with a word that starts with the same letter. For instance, Nancy could say, "I'm Nancy Noodle."

2. Now the second player says his name and follows it with a word that starts with the same letter. For instance, Bobby could say, "I'm Bobby Bully." But then Bobby must also say, "And that's Nancy Noodle."

3. Now it is the third player's turn. Let's pretend it is Andrew. Andrew would say "I'm Andrew Applesauce." Then he would add, "And that's Billy Bully, and Nancy Noodle."

4. Keep going around the circle until everyone has had a turn.

BOO-BOO
AND EMILY JUNIOR

(also known as Cat and Mouse)
a game for two players

Everybody knows a cat and a mouse (or a rat) can't be friends. But this silly game is always played by two friends. And this time you can't use your indoor voice or your outdoor voice. You have to be really, really quiet!

You will need:

a dining room table, two blindfolds

Here's how you play:

Both players put on blindfolds. One player is the cat and one is the mouse. The cat must try to catch the mouse. The mouse must try to keep from getting caught. The players move around the dining room table — always keeping their fingertips on the table. (You'll have to move the chairs away from the table to play this game.) Everything has to be done as quietly as possible so the mouse won't hear the cat, and the cat won't hear the mouse. You might even want to take off your shoes. When the cat touches the mouse, the game is over.

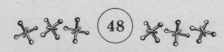

LET'S DO THE TWIST

tongue twisters for one or more players!

Twist your tongue with these tongue twisters. Remember to say them three times fast!

Karen cooks cookies quickly.

Bully Bobby bled bad blue blood.

Round and round the ragged rocks, ragged Ricky ran!

Pamela's so selfish she should sell shellfish shells. But shellfish shells seldom sell.

GETTING THE GIGGLES

a game for five or more players

Some silly things go on in Ms. Colman's class. The kids put on their clothes backwards for Backwards Day. Karen dresses like a turkey for the Thanksgiving play. But nothing cracks the kids up like this game!

The setup:

Everyone lies faceup on the floor. Each player puts his or her head on the stomach of the player ahead of him or her.

Here's how you play:

The first person says, "Ha!" Then the next person says, "Ha ha," the next person says, "Ha ha ha," and so on. When you reach the end, start all over again, with even *more* "ha ha has!"

When people giggle, their tummies bounce up and down. That can feel pretty funny when your head is resting on one of those bouncing tummies. Before you know it, everyone will have the giggles!

WHAT TIME IS IT, MR. FOX?

a game for five or more players

Ever since Andrew learned how to tell time, he's been begging Karen and her friends to play this game. And they always seem to find the time to play What Time Is It, Mr. Fox?

The setup:

One player is the fox. Everyone else is a bunny. The bunnies stand in a line about 20 feet away from Mr. Fox.

Here's how you play:

1. Mr. Fox turns his back to the bunnies.
2. The bunnies say, "What time is it, Mr. Fox?" Mr. Fox shouts out a time. The number tells the bunnies how many steps to take. For example, if Mr. Fox says it is eight o'clock, the bunnies take 8 steps toward Mr. Fox. If Mr. Fox says it is two o'clock, the bunnies take two steps. After all the bunnies have taken their steps, they repeat the question, "What time is it, Mr. Fox?"
3. Mr. Fox keeps calling out times until he senses one of the bunnies coming up close to him. Then Mr. Fox shouts out, "It's midnight!"
4. Mr. Fox turns around and chases all the bunnies, who must scatter across the playing field.
5. The first bunny tapped by Mr. Fox becomes the new Mr. Fox.

CLOUDY WITH A CHANCE OF ICE CREAM

a game for one or more players

This is a game you have to play outside. But since it is a very quiet kind of game, lots of kids use their indoor voices anyway.

Here's how you play:

Wait for a sunny day when there are just a few fluffy clouds in the sky. All the players lie on their backs and stare at the clouds. The players must take turns pointing to different clouds and saying what they think the clouds look like. Anybody see a vanilla ice cream cone? How about a butterfly in a ski cap?

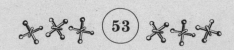

TRAIN TAG

a game for six or more players

Karen has traveled on a bus, in a car, and on an airplane. But in this game she gets to be part of a train. So will you.

Ready now? Everybody shout..."All aboard!"

Here's how you play:

1. Four players link their arms together. They are the first four cars in the train. They cannot let go of one another. They have to run with their arms linked.
2. All the players in the train run around, shouting "Choo choo!" in their loudest outdoor voices. The other players try to run away. The members of the train try to catch as many of the other players as they can by forming a circle around them.
3. If a player is circled, she must join arms with the others on the train. She is now another car in the train, and she must help capture the other players.
4. The game is over when everyone has been caught and become part of the train.

SNAP THE WHIP

a game for six or more players

It's the Three Musketeers versus the Milky Ways! Who will win?

You will need:

two handkerchiefs or scarves of equal length

Here's how you play:

1. Split yourselves evenly into two teams. Each team forms a straight line, one player in front of the other. Each player holds onto the teammate in front of her by placing her arms around his or her waist. No one is allowed to let go.
2. The last person in each line tucks the end of one handkerchief into his or her pocket.
3. It is up to the first person in line to snatch the handkerchief from the last person in the other team's line.
4. The first team to get the other team's handkerchief wins.

REALLY GREAT RELAYS!
races for four or more players

On your mark, get set, go! Ms. Colman's class had a great time running these relays at their class picnic. But you don't need the whole class to try these relay races. Two teams of two kids each will work out just fine!

JELL-O EVERYONE!

You will need:
   two sets of chopsticks, two paper or plastic cereal bowls, 12 squares of Jell-O (any flavor), two paper plates

The setup:
   Place six squares of Jell-O on each paper plate. Place the paper plates at the starting line. Place the bowls about 20 feet away from the starting line.

Here's how you play:
1. As soon as someone yells, "Go," the first player on each team picks up a square of Jell-O with the chopsticks.
2. Holding the Jell-O between the chopsticks, the players run to the bowls.
3. The players drop the Jell-O squares into the bowls and run back to the starting line, passing the chopsticks to the next player on the team. If the player drops the Jell-O, he must go back and pick up another square.

4. The first team to get two Jell-O squares in the bowl wins.

There is always a chance that neither team will get two Jell-O squares in the bowl. If that happens, wait until there are no Jell-O squares left. Then, the first team to get one square in the bowl wins.

PING-PONG PLOP!

You will need:
   two Ping-Pong balls, a piece of string

The setup:
Place the string on the ground, 20 feet from the starting line.

Here's how you play:

1. As soon as someone yells, "Go," the first player on each team gets down on all fours and places a Ping-Pong ball on her back.
2. Each player must crawl over to the string and then back to the starting point with the ball on her back. If she drops the Ping-Pong ball, she must pick it up and crawl back to the starting line to start all over again. Once she successfully crawls up and back with the ball on her back, she passes the ball on to the next player on her team.
3. The first team to have all of its players go successfully back and forth wins.

JUMPIN' JACKS

Calling all Jacks...and all Jills, too! It's time to play jacks!

There are lots and lots of games you can play with ten jacks and a small rubber ball. Here are some of the Three Musketeers' favorites!

Karen's helpful hint:

These instructions are for kids who are right-handed. If you're a lefty, use your left hand wherever the instructions say to use your right hand.

THE BASIC JACKS GAME

a game for one or more players

You will need:

ten jacks, one small rubber ball, a hard, flat playing surface

Here's how you play:

1. Place all the jacks in your right hand. With a single sweeping motion, scatter the jacks on the floor.
2. Using your right hand, toss the ball up in the air, pick up one jack, and catch the ball after it bounces.

3. Hold the jack in your left hand. Repeat step 2. Add the second jack to your left hand.
4. Keep going until you have picked up all ten jacks one at a time. If at any time you miss the ball, you miss a jack, or you move a jack without picking it up — your turn is over. After you've picked up all ten jacks, you've finished onesies.
5. Now you move on to twosies. Repeat step 1.
6. Repeat steps 2 and 3. But this time pick up two jacks at once. Continue picking up two jacks at a time until you've picked up all ten, completing twosies.
7. Keep playing until you have finished threesies (three sets of three jacks and one jack); foursies (two set of four jacks and one set of two jacks); fivesies (two sets of five jacks); sixies (one set of six jacks, and one set of four jacks); sevensies (one set of seven jacks and one set of three jacks); eightsies (one set of eight jacks and one set of two jacks); ninesies (one set of nine jacks and one jack); and tensies (all ten jacks at once). Then go backwards from tensies to onesies.
8. When one player misses, it is the next player's turn. At each new turn, a player picks up at the number she was on when she missed. For example, if you were in the middle of foursies when you missed, at your next turn start at the beginning of foursies.
9. The first player to go all the way up to tensies and back down to onesies wins.

SWEEPING THE FLOOR

a game for one or more players

Here's how you play:

1. Place all the jacks in your right hand. With a single, sweeping motion, scatter the jacks on the floor.
2. Toss the ball into the air with your right hand. As the ball bounces one time, place your hand on a jack and sweep it toward your body. (Do not lift it off the floor.) Then quickly pick up the jack and catch the ball.
3. Go through onesies, twosies, threesies, and so on.

As in the basic game, if you miss the ball, move a jack, or fail to sweep and pick up a jack, your turn is through.

SCRUBBING THE FLOOR

a game for one or more players

Here's how you play:

1. Repeat steps 1 and 2 for Sweeping the Floor.
2. After the ball bounces one time, grab one jack in your right hand and scrub it across the floor in a backwards and forwards movement. Then quickly catch the ball with your right hand.

3. Now hold the jack in your left hand.
4. Keep playing up to tensies and back down again to onesies.

EVERYBODY UP, EVERYBODY DOWN!

a game for one or more players

Here's how you play:
1. Place all the jacks and the ball in your right hand.
2. Toss the ball but hold onto the jacks. (If any jacks slip out when you toss, your turn is over.) While the ball is in the air, scatter the jacks. After the ball bounces, catch it in your right hand.

3. Toss the ball into the air again. Sweep up all ten jacks in your right hand, and catch the ball *before* it bounces.
4. Keep going until you miss. Let each player have a turn. The player who can do it the most wins.

TRIVIA TWIST

Put a Little Sister Twist on your jacks games. In this jacks game, each player must answer a Baby-sitters Little Sister question before taking her turn. Use the questions on this page, or make up some of your own. Check on page 69 for the answers to these questions.

1. There are two monsters in *Karen's Monsters*. One is Frankenstone, the monster Charlie is building for the Halloween parade. The other is someone in the big house. Who does Karen call a monster?
2. When Karen goes on a winter trip to Shadow Lake, what does she discover she doesn't like to do?
3. What is the name of Karen's pony in Baby-sitters Little Sister #60?
4. What are the names of Karen's and Andrew's goldfish?
5. What does Karen think Druscilla Porter is?
6. Someone was really mean to Karen when she first got her glasses. But then that same classmate got glasses. Who got the glasses?
7. What kind of jewelry did Karen's dad give Kristy in *Karen's Big Sister*?
8. Karen can't keep a secret. What have her classmates nicknamed her?

JUST STRINGING YOU ALONG!

One day, Karen, Hannie, and Nancy had nothing to do. So, Nannie gave them a piece of string to play with — just like the one you'll find in this kit. What can you do with a piece of string? You'll be amazed!

Karen's helpful hint:

These string designs are really tough to make. But if you follow the pictures, and practice really hard, you'll be making them in no time! And boy, will you be proud of yourself!

MORBIDDA DESTINY'S BROOM

a string design for one player

You will need:

the string in the *Baby-sitters Little Sister Playground Games* kit

Here's what you do:

1. Place your hands with your palms facing each other. Wrap the string behind your left thumb and your pinky. Do the same with your right hand so the string is around your hands like it is in picture A.
2. Move your right pointer finger under the string on your left palm. Pull your right hand back with the string around your pointer finger.
3. Carefully twirl your right index finger once so there is a twist in the string. (See picture B.)
4. Take your left pointer finger and go down through

the loop on your right pointer finger and under the string across your right palm. (See picture C.)

5. Drop the strings that are on your right thumb and right pinky. Now pull back slowly.
6. Pull both hands back. (See picture D.)

Be careful, Morbidda Destiny might fly off on that broom any minute now!

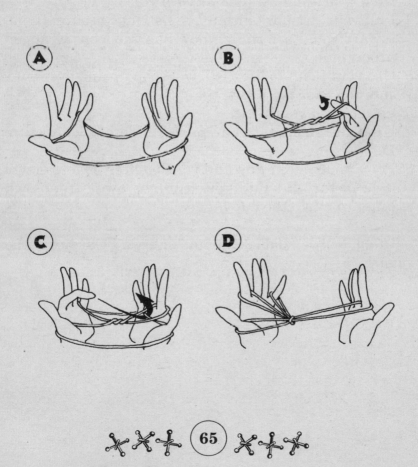

KAREN'S TEA PARTY

a string design for one player

Here's what you do:
1. Repeat steps 1 and 2 of Morbidda Destiny's Broom.
2. Place your left pointer finger under the string on your right palm. Pull that string all the way back to your right hand. (See picture A.)
3. Move your thumbs over the pointer strings closest to your thumbs and under the pointer strings farthest from your thumbs. (See picture B.)
4. Pull your thumbs, with all the strings around them, toward you. Each thumb now has two loops wrapped around it.
5. Use your teeth to lift the lower loop up and over your thumbs. (See picture C.)
6. Let go with your teeth.
7. Drop the string off your pinky fingers. (See picture D.)
8. Point your thumbs up and your pointer fingers down. (See picture E.) Pull your thumbs away from each other to make the cup bigger.

Ta-da! You've made a cup and saucer. Please pass the sugar!

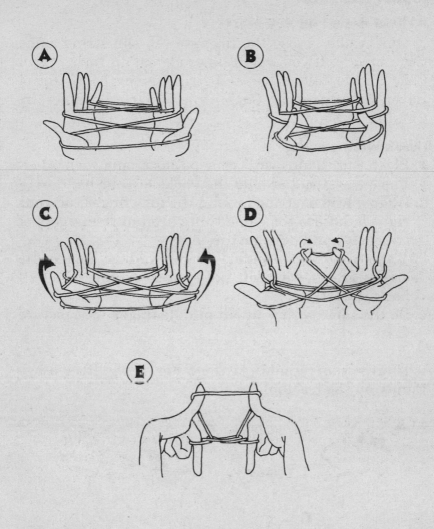

DANNY'S CRADLE
a string design for one player

This cradle is also the first step in the string game Cat's Cradle. If you would like to learn all the steps in Cat's Cradle, take a look at a string games book. One of Karen's favorites is *Cat's Cradle String Games* by Camilla Gryski.

Here's what you do:
1. Place your hands with your palms facing each other. Place the string around the backs of your hands.
2. Wrap a loop of string around the four fingers on your right hand. Do the same thing around the fingers of your left hand. (See picture A.)
3. Take your right middle finger and go under the string across your left palm. (See picture B.) Pull back the string.
4. Do the same with your left middle finger. (See picture C.)

There's your cradle. All together now, "Rock-a-bye Danny on the treetop..."

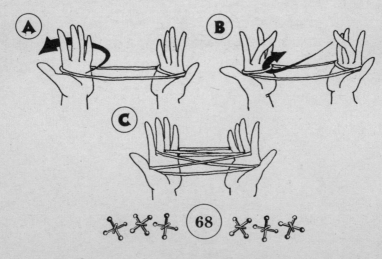

ANSWERS

Answer to the Super Silly Puzzle

Answers to the Trivia Twist

1. Emily Michelle 2. ski 3. Blueberry 4. Crystal Light the Second and Goldfishie 5. a witch 6. Ricky 7. a pin 8. Blarin' Karen

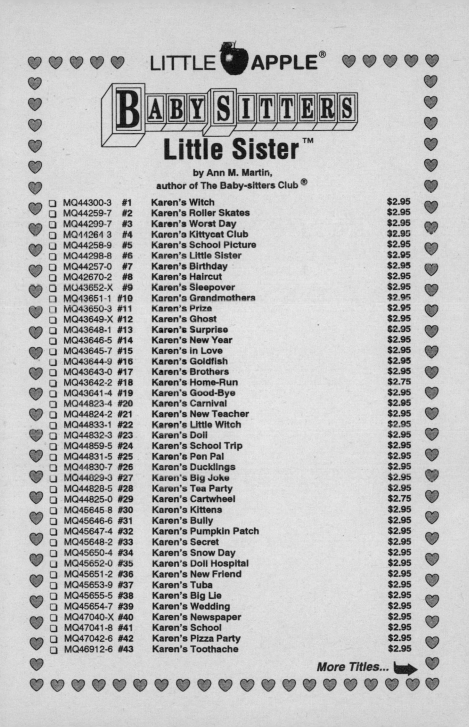

LITTLE APPLE®

BABYSITTERS
Little Sister™

by Ann M. Martin,
author of The Baby-sitters Club®

☐	MQ44300-3	#1	Karen's Witch	$2.95
☐	MQ44259-7	#2	Karen's Roller Skates	$2.95
☐	MQ44299-7	#3	Karen's Worst Day	$2.95
☐	MQ44264-3	#4	Karen's Kittycat Club	$2.95
☐	MQ44258-9	#5	Karen's School Picture	$2.95
☐	MQ44298-8	#6	Karen's Little Sister	$2.95
☐	MQ44257-0	#7	Karen's Birthday	$2.95
☐	MQ42670-2	#8	Karen's Haircut	$2.95
☐	MQ43652-X	#9	Karen's Sleepover	$2.95
☐	MQ43651-1	#10	Karen's Grandmothers	$2.95
☐	MQ43650-3	#11	Karen's Prize	$2.95
☐	MQ43649-X	#12	Karen's Ghost	$2.95
☐	MQ43648-1	#13	Karen's Surprise	$2.95
☐	MQ43646-5	#14	Karen's New Year	$2.95
☐	MQ43645-7	#15	Karen's in Love	$2.95
☐	MQ43644-9	#16	Karen's Goldfish	$2.95
☐	MQ43643-0	#17	Karen's Brothers	$2.95
☐	MQ43642-2	#18	Karen's Home-Run	$2.75
☐	MQ43641-4	#19	Karen's Good-Bye	$2.95
☐	MQ44823-4	#20	Karen's Carnival	$2.95
☐	MQ44824-2	#21	Karen's New Teacher	$2.95
☐	MQ44833-1	#22	Karen's Little Witch	$2.95
☐	MQ44832-3	#23	Karen's Doll	$2.95
☐	MQ44859-5	#24	Karen's School Trip	$2.95
☐	MQ44831-5	#25	Karen's Pen Pal	$2.95
☐	MQ44830-7	#26	Karen's Ducklings	$2.95
☐	MQ44829-3	#27	Karen's Big Joke	$2.95
☐	MQ44828-5	#28	Karen's Tea Party	$2.95
☐	MQ44825-0	#29	Karen's Cartwheel	$2.75
☐	MQ45645-8	#30	Karen's Kittens	$2.95
☐	MQ45646-6	#31	Karen's Bully	$2.95
☐	MQ45647-4	#32	Karen's Pumpkin Patch	$2.95
☐	MQ45648-2	#33	Karen's Secret	$2.95
☐	MQ45650-4	#34	Karen's Snow Day	$2.95
☐	MQ45652-0	#35	Karen's Doll Hospital	$2.95
☐	MQ45651-2	#36	Karen's New Friend	$2.95
☐	MQ45653-9	#37	Karen's Tuba	$2.95
☐	MQ45655-5	#38	Karen's Big Lie	$2.95
☐	MQ45654-7	#39	Karen's Wedding	$2.95
☐	MQ47040-X	#40	Karen's Newspaper	$2.95
☐	MQ47041-8	#41	Karen's School	$2.95
☐	MQ47042-6	#42	Karen's Pizza Party	$2.95
☐	MQ46912-6	#43	Karen's Toothache	$2.95

More Titles... ➡